Phonics *Plus* K
Student Edition

John F. Savage, EdD

Professor Emeritus
Lynch School of Education
Boston College

Consultants

Francine R. Johnston, EdD
University of North Carolina at Greensboro
Phonics and Phonological Awareness

Melanie R. Kuhn, PhD
Rutgers University
Fluency

Melinda S. Rice, PhD
Elon University
Comprehension

Cindy A. Strickland, MA
University of Virginia
Differentiated Instruction

Illustrator

Chris Sabatino

EDUCATORS PUBLISHING SERVICE
Cambridge and Toronto

Thank You

This program is dedicated to the many thousands of teachers and other educators who are devoted to helping children become competent and confident readers and writers.

Enormous thanks are due to the many people who had a hand in bringing *Phonics Plus* from concept to reality. Specifically:

- Charlie Heinle and the leadership at Educators Publishing Service for their vision in recognizing the need to create a program that would meet the varied literacy needs of all children
- The team of skilled professionals who wrote the Differentiated Instruction Guides: Beth Davis, Mileidis Gort, and Renée Greenfield
- The several consultants who lent their insight and expertise as the program was being written: Melinda Rice, Cindy Strickland, and Melanie Kuhn. Especially helpful was the advice of Francine Johnston whose involvement began at the beginning and continued to the end
- Design consultant Jennifer Nelson and content consultant Judy Nyberg, who reviewed materials at later stages in development
- Teachers who shared their insights and critical comments to refine the content and approach of many of the activities
- The staff at Educators Publishing Service, particularly Kate Moltz, editor extraordinaire, and Stacey Nichols Kim whose skill and support were ceaseless. Thanks to Eryn Kline for her help with permissions and to Heather Terry for making my ideas look so attractive on the page

Each of these people contributed his or her time and talent in helping make this program part of children's instructional lives.

—John Savage

Acquisitions/Development: Kate Moltz
Senior Editor: Stacey Nichols Kim
Senior Editorial Manager: Sheila Neylon

Senior Designers: Heather Terry and Karen Lomigora
Typesetter: Sarah Rakitin
Cover Design: David Parra

ISBN 0-8388-1015

Printed in U.S.A.

Contents

Unit 1

Unit 2

Unit 3

Unit 4

Parent Letter

Dear Parents,

Your child is beginning an important and exciting adventure: learning to read. You have been helping your child learn since he or she was born. Now your child needs your help as he or she begins kindergarten.

You are extremely important in helping your child become a successful reader and writer. What can you do?

- *Read aloud to your child every day.* Hearing stories and poems helps your child realize how much fun reading can be. Reading aloud gives your child important experiences with books and makes them a part of everyday life.

- *Call attention to letters and sounds.* Recite the alphabet as you put your child to bed. Look for letters as you ride the bus or walk through the mall. Call attention to words that rhyme, words like *yummy* and *tummy*, *car* and *far*.

- *Get involved in your child's learning.* Talk to your child about what is going on in school. Proudly display your child's schoolwork at home.

- Some of the pages your child will bring home from this book have activities on them for you to do together. These activities are at the bottom of the page, marked with this symbol 📖 . Help your child practice new skills by doing these fun, simple exercises together.

As they begin kindergarten, children need to be surrounded by language, learning, and love. As your child's first teachers, these are gifts only you can give.

Sincerely,

John F. Savage

Carta a los Padres

Queridos padres:

Su hijo/hija está a punto de comenzar una aventura importante y emocionante: aprender a leer. Usted le ha estado ayudando a aprender desde que nació. Ahora él o ella necesita su ayuda al comenzar el jardín de infancia. Su ayuda es fundamental para el desarrollo de las habilidades lectoras y escritoras de su hijo/hija. ¿Cómo puede ayudar?

- *Leyendo en voz alta a su hijo/hija cada día.* Escuchar cuentos y poemas les ayuda a darse cuenta de lo divertida que puede ser la lectura. Leer en voz alta le aporta una experiencia importante con los libros, que así pasan a formar parte de su vida diaria.

- *Llamando su atención hacia las letras y los sonidos.* Recite el alfabeto cuando le vaya a acostar a su hijo/hija. Busquen letras cuando vayan en el autobús o cuando paseen por el centro comercial. Llame su atención hacia palabras que riman, como llama y cama, gato y pato.

- *Involucrándose en su aprendizaje.* Hablen de lo que su hijo/hija está haciendo en la escuela. Exhiba con orgullo los trabajos que traiga a casa

- Algunas páginas de este libro que traerá a casa contienen actividades para que las realicen juntos/as. Estas actividades se encuentran en la parte inferior de la página y están indicadas con este símbolo 📖. Ayúdele a su hijo/hija a practicar nuevas destrezas haciendo estos divertidos y sencillos ejercicios juntos/as.

Cuando empiezan el jardín de infancia, es necesario ofrecerles a los niños mucha práctica con el lenguaje, ayudarles con el aprendizaje y rodearlos de cariño. En calidad de primer maestro/maestra de su hijo, estos son regalos que sólo usted puede hacerles.

Atentamente,

John F. Savage

Twinkle, Twinkle Little Star

Twinkle, twinkle little star,
How I wonder what you are.
Up above the world so high,
Like a diamond in the sky.
Twinkle, twinkle little star,
How I wonder what you are.

a

1 Read this poem with me.

3

Tree Bear

Listen to the tree bear
Crying in the night
Crying for his mommy
In the pale moonlight.
What will his mommy do
When she hears him cry?
Tuck him in a cocoa pod
And sing a lullaby.

for

Why is tree bear crying?

4

Tree Bear's Rhymes

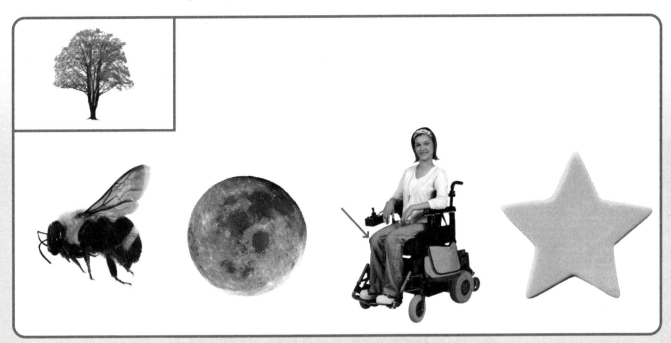

 As you say "goodnight" to your child, sing a lullaby or recite a favorite rhyme.

2b Box 1: Circle the pictures whose names rhyme with *tree*.
Box 2: Circle the pictures whose names rhyme with *bear*.

Jack and Jill

Jack and Jill went up the hill
To fetch a pail of water.
Jack fell down
And broke his crown,
And Jill came tumbling after.

the

Help your child make a rhyme out of his or her name or nickname like the one in the poem: *Jill/hill*.

6

3a   Listen as I read this poem. Circle the picture that shows what's happening at the *beginning* of the poem.

Jill's Rhymes

7

3b | Circle the pictures whose names rhyme with *pail*.

The Cat and the Fiddle

Hey, diddle, diddle!
The cat and the fiddle.
The cow jumped over the moon;
The little dog laughed to see such sport
And the dish ran away with the spoon.

 With your child, make up a silly story about household objects running away together, like the dish and the spoon.

4a   Listen as I read this poem. Circle the happy face if the words rhyme and the sad face if they don't.

Cat and Dog Rhymes

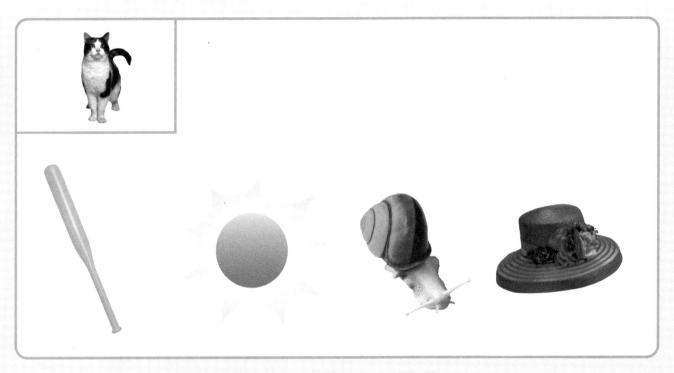

 Help your child think of more words that rhyme with *cat* and *dog*. Post the list and add to it as you think of more words.

4b | Box 1: Circle the pictures whose names rhyme with *cat*.
Box 2: Circle the pictures whose names rhyme with *dog*.

Star Words: *the, a*

Up above the world so high,
Like a diamond in the sky.

Jack and Jill went up the hill
To fetch a pail of water.

5a | Trace the Star Words with your finger. Follow along as
I read the phrases and circle the Star Words you hear.

Star Words: *for, is*

Tree bear is crying.
He is crying for his mommy.

Jack is a boy.
Jill is a girl.

 Point out the very common Star Words *for* and *is* as you and your child do things together, both at home and in the community.

11

5b Trace the Star Words with your finger. Follow along as I read the phrases and circle the Star Words you hear.

Rebus Reading with Star Words

1. A  is for the  .

2. The  is for the  .

3. The is for the  .

As your family sets the table for a meal, say for example, "The soup is _____ Tonia." Let children add the word *for* to complete the sentence.

6a   Read each sentence to a partner. Point to each word and picture as you read.

Name _____

Cross the Bridge

Play a game of sorting objects by shape: round, square, rectangle, and so on. See how many shapes your child can sort in a given time.

6b Draw a line from each hole in the bridge to the shape that will fill that hole.

13

Alphabet Song

A B C D E F G

H I J K

L M N O P

Q R S

T U V

W X

Y Z

Now I know my A B Cs,
Next time won't you
sing with me?

7a Sing the Alphabet Song. Circle the letters that are in your first name. Look at your name card for help.

Name _____

Connect the Dots

A B E F I J
M N
C D G H K
L

Z

O

U T

Y V S P

X W R Q

7b | Connect the letters of the alphabet in order. What did you draw?

Alphabet Overview

A a   G g

B b   H h

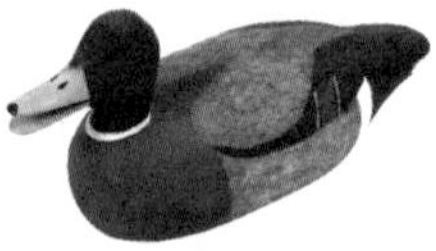

C c   I i

D d   J j

E e   K k

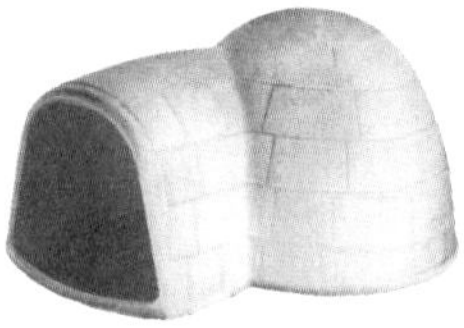

F f   L l

M m		**T t**	
N n		**U u**	
O o		**V v**	
P p		**W w**	
Q q		**X x**	
R r		**Y y**	
S s		**Z z**	

8   Read the alphabet with me. Say each key word's name. Then follow the directions that I give you.

A Silly Poem

I see an **A**nt, I see a **B**oat,
I see a **C**at upon my coat.

I see a **D**uck, I see an **E**gg,
I see a **F**ish upon my leg.

I see a **G**oat, I see a **H**at,
I see an **I**gloo on my mat.

I see a **J**ar, I see a **K**ing,
I see a **L**eaf perched on my swing.

I see the **M**oon, I see a **N**est,
I see an **O**ctopus on my vest.

Blocks

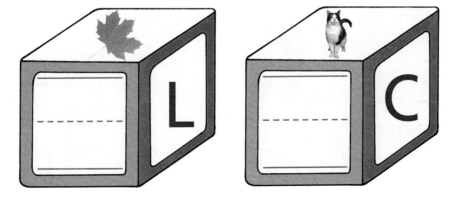

11b Write the partner capital letter on each block in the first set.
Write the partner lowercase letter each block in the second set.

Hickory, Dickory, Dock!

Hickory, dickory, dock!
The mouse ran up the clock;
The clock struck one,
The mouse ran down,
Hickory, dickory, dock!

What did the mouse do?

Which two pictures rhyme with *dock* and *clock*?

 As you say the rhyme with your child, help him or her find the numbers on a clock.

12a | Follow along as we read this poem together. Circle the picture that answers the question I ask.

Name _____

New Rhyme

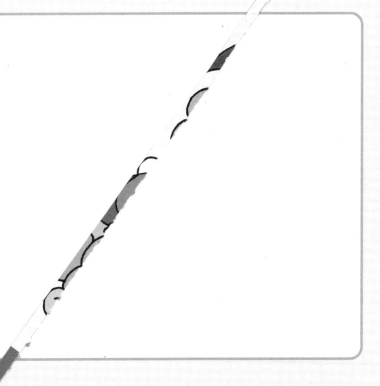

 With your child, find rhyming words for other words in this rhyme: *down*, *ran*, *one*, and so on.

12b Box 1: Draw a picture of something that rhymes with *mouse*.
Box 2: Draw a picture of something that rhymes with *clock*.

Rhyming Colors

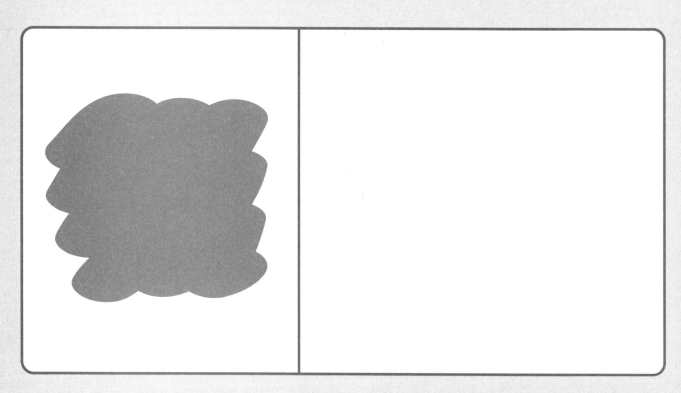

 With your child, do a Color Find around the house. Look for things that are pink, green, purple, and so on.

13a | Box 1: Draw a picture of something that rhymes with red. Color it red.
Box 2: Draw a picture of something that rhymes with blue. Color it blue.

"I Can," Said the Man

"What's that?" said the   .

"A house," said the   .

"Of course," said the   .

"What now?" said the   .

"I'm asleep," said the   .

13b Listen as I read these sentences. Then circle the animal whose name rhymes with the orange word.

Two Little Eyes

Two little eyes to look around,
Two little ears to hear each sound;
One little nose to smell what's sweet,
One little mouth that likes to eat.

14a Follow along as we read this poem together.
Then act the poem out with me.

Name _____

Self-Portrait

[blank drawing box]

_____

- -

Name _____

 Talk about this self-portrait with your child. Encourage her or him to add details.

14b Draw a picture of yourself. Include your eyes, ears, nose, and mouth. Add something that you like to see, hear, smell, or taste.

Star Words: *in, on, have, has*

---

1. The is in the .

2. The is on the .

3. The has a .

4. The have  .

15a | Trace the Star Words with your finger.
Read each sentence to a partner.

Review Star Words

the   a   is   for

in   on   have   has

1. The bear is in a tree.

2. The cow is on the moon.

3. Jill has a pail.

4. The pail is for Jack.

5. Jack and Jill have water.

15b | Listen while I read the sentences. Circle all the Star Words you hear. Draw a picture to go with one of the sentences.

Missing Blocks

16a | Write the missing capital letters on the blocks.

Have your child suggest alternative pictures for the blocks, for example, b/bear; h/house, and so on.

16b Write the missing lowercase letters on the blocks.

Vowels and Consonants

Read all the letters on the keyboard. Color the vowels red.
Color the consonants blue. Trace the vowels in each box.

Alphabet Maze

17b Peter can only step on vowels. Mark the letters that will help Peter get home.

Syllables

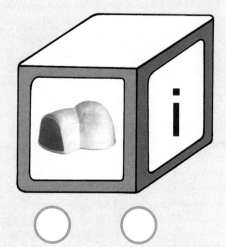

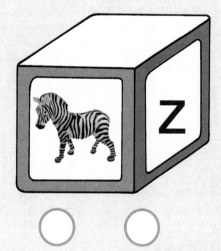

 Say a list of words aloud. Have your child use pennies, buttons, or other small markers to indicate the number of syllables they hear in each word.

18a | Color one dot if the word has one syllable.
Color two dots if the word has two syllables.

Name _____

Syllables

18b Color one dot if the word has one syllable. Color two dots if it has two syllables. Color three dots if it has three syllables.

Review Star Words

the · a · is · for

in · on · have · has

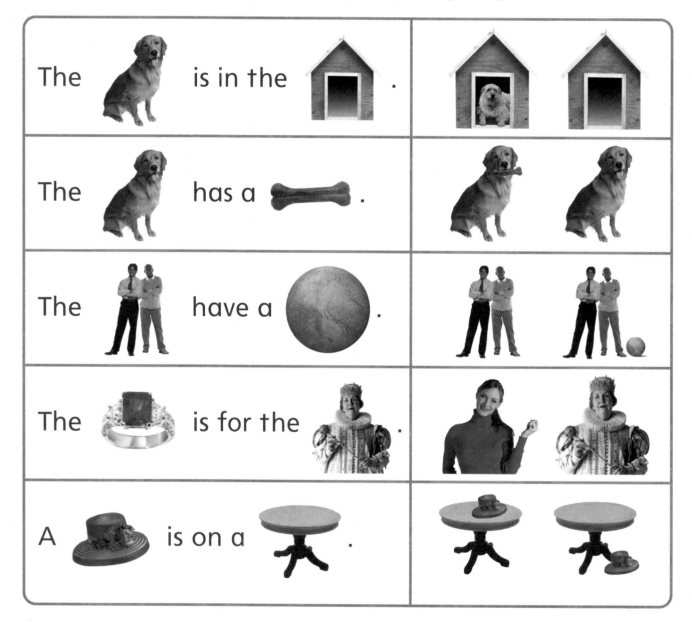

The 🐕 is in the 🏠 .

The 🐕 has a 🦴 .

The 👥 have a ⚪ .

The 💍 is for the 👑 .

A 👒 is on a 🪑 .

Ask your child to read any of the Star Words that you see while reading.

19a — Circle the correct picture for each sentence.

Print All Around

19b Circle all the words you see in this picture. Tell a story about what happens in the picture. Be sure the story has a beginning, a middle, and an end.

Parent Letter

Dear Parents,

During the coming weeks and months, your child will continue the exciting adventure of reading by learning more about the letters of the alphabet and the sounds that these letters represent. Knowing letters and sounds is essential to success in beginning reading.

There is much you can do at home to support your child's learning. Keep doing the *Phonics Plus* exercises marked with this icon 📖. And you can call your child's attention to the letters all around you and to the sounds that these letters represent. For example:

- In the car, on the bus, or on the subway, say things like, "Let's see how many times we see the letter *T* for *Tamara* between here and the supermarket."

- At the mall, say, "Let's find all the *D*s for *Diego* as we walk along."

- In the kitchen, say, "Look at the *M* on the milk carton; milk starts with *m-m-m-m*, just like *M-M-Michele* and *m-m-mommy*."

Simple comments like this will help your child make connections between the letters and sounds needed in learning to read.

Of course, it's still important for you to read to your child every day, to visit the library, to talk to your child about school, and to show interest and pride in the work your child brings home.

Make this the most exciting time in your child's life.

Sincerely,

John F. Savage

Carta a los Padres

Queridos padres:

Durante las siguientes semanas y meses, su hijo/hija continuará la emocionante aventura de aprender a leer profundizando en el aprendizaje de las letras del alfabeto y los sonidos representados por estas letras. El conocimiento de las letras y los sonidos es esencial para progresar adecuadamente en el nivel inicial de lectura.

Usted puede hacer mucho desde casa para apoyar el aprendizaje de su hijo/hija. Sigan realizando los ejercicios de *Phonics Plus* indicados con este símbolo. Puede llamar su atención hacia las letras que les rodean y los sonidos que representan. Por ejemplo:

- En el carro, en el autobús o en el metro, diga algo así: "Vamos a contar las veces que vemos la letra *T* de *Tamara* de aquí al supermercado".

- En el centro comercial, diga: "Busquemos todas las letras *D* de *Diego* mientras paseamos".

- En la cocina, diga: "Mira la letra *L* en el cartón de leche; leche empieza por *l-l-l-l*, como *L-L-Laura* y *l-l-lagartija*".

Comentarios sencillos como éste le ayudarán a su hijo/hija a relacionar las letras y los sonidos, algo que resulta esencial para aprender a leer.

Claro, todavía es importante que usted lea a su hijo/hija cada día, que vayan a la biblioteca, que hablen de lo que hace en la escuela, y que muestre interés y orgullo por los trabajos que traiga a casa.

Haga que ésta sea la época más emocionante de la vida de su hijo/hija.

Atentamente,

John F. Savage

A Was an Apple Pie

A was an apple pie.
B bit it
C cut it
D dealt it
E et it
F fought for it
G got it
H had it
I inspected it
J joined it
K kept it
L longed for it
M mourned for it

N nodded at it

O opened it

P peeped in it

Q quartered it

R ran for it

S stole it

T took it

U upset it

V viewed it

W wanted it

XYZ & ampersand

All wished for

A piece in hand.

it

What would you do to an apple pie?

20 | Listen while I read this poem. Then talk about the question at the end.

Skyscraper

Skyscraper, skyscraper,
Scrape me some sky:
Tickle the sun
While the stars go by.

—Dennis Lee

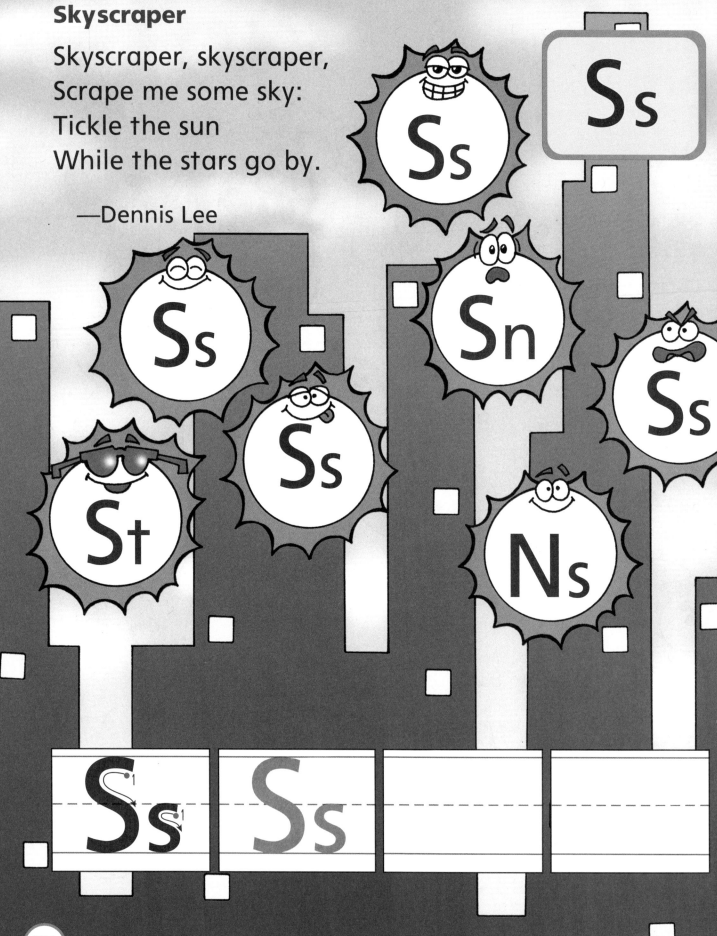

21a Color the suns with the partner letters *Ss*. Write the letters *Ss* on the lines.

Initial Consonant /s/

Six silly seals sip soup slowly.

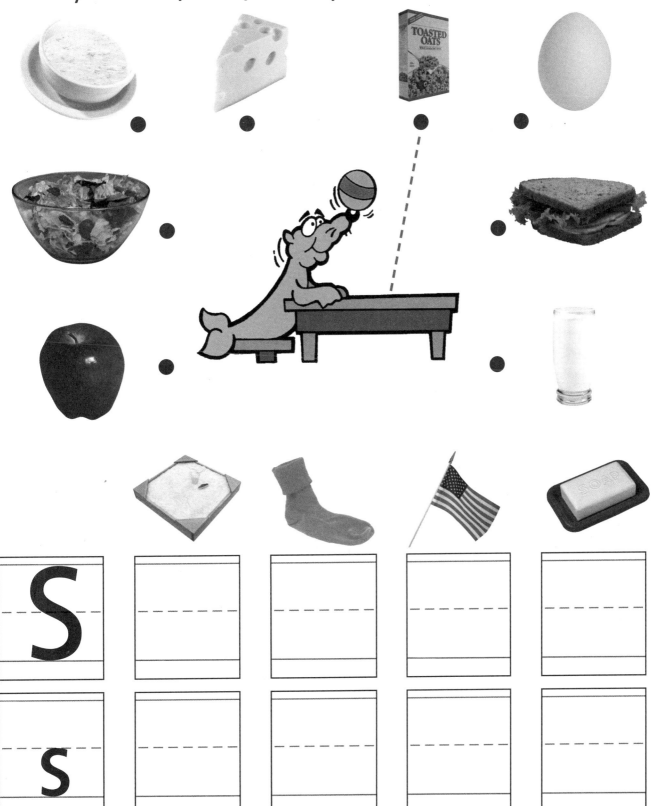

21b Draw a line from the foods that begin with /s/ to the table.
Write Ss under the pictures whose names begin with /s/.

To Market

To market, to market,
  to buy a new pig.
Home again, home again, jiggedy jig.
To market, to market,
  to buy a new hog.
Home again, home again, jiggedy jog.

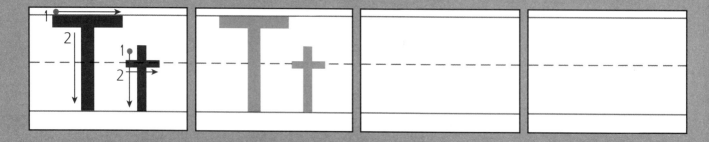

22a · Color the turtles with the partner letters *Tt*. Write the letters *Tt* on the lines.

Initial Consonant /t/

Tim told Tina to take her turn.

22b | Circle the pictures whose names begin with /t/. Write *Tt* under the pictures whose names begin with /t/.

The North Wind

The north wind does blow,
And we will have snow,
And what will poor robin do then,
    poor thing?

N n

and

Color the nests with the partner letters *Nn*. Write the letters *Nn* on the lines.

Initial Consonant /n/

Nine nice nurses nibble noodles nightly.

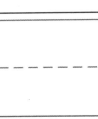

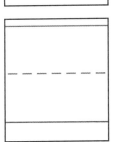

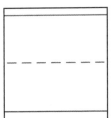
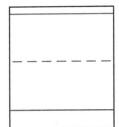

N

n

23b | Draw a line connecting the pictures whose names begin with /n/. Write *Nn* under the pictures whose names begin with /n/.

Lucy Locket

Lucy Locket lost her pocket.
　Kitty Fisher found it.
Not a penny was there in it,
　But a ribbon 'round it.

24a | Color the leaves with the partner letters *Ll*. Write the letters *Ll* on the lines.

Initial Consonant /l/

Lazy lions like lemon and lime lollipops.

24b | Draw a line from the pictures whose names begin with /l/ to the dots in the ladder. Write Ll under the pictures whose names begin with /l/.

Covers

Glass covers windows
to keep the cold away
Clouds cover the sky
to make a rainy day

—Nikki Giovanni

Cc Lc

Cn Nc

Cc

25a   Color the cats with the partner letters *Cc*. Write the letters *Cc* on the lines.

Initial Consonant c as /k/

Cute cats cuddle in a cozy cottage.

HAPPY FARM

MILK

C

c

25b (top) Color all the objects in the picture that start with /k/.
(bottom) If the picture's name begins with /c/, write Cc on the lines.

Review Initial Consonants /s/ and /t/

 Help your child make a sentence using the /t/ words on the page and a sentence using the /s/ words on the page.

Write *Tt* on the line if the picture's name begins with /t/.
Write *Ss* on the line if the picture's name begins with /s/.

Review Initial Consonants /n/, /l/, and c as /k/

26b In each row, circle the three pictures whose names begin with the same sound.

Connect the Letters and Sounds

27a Draw lines connecting each pair of capital and lowercase letters.

Name _____

Matching Sounds

c
t
l

s
n
t

l
c
n

t
n
s

n
c
s

t
n
l

 Help your child practice writing the
letter he or she chose for each item.

27b Circle the first letter of
each picture's name.

Blending Onsets and Rimes

1.

2.

3.

4.

5.

28a Listen as I say some words in two parts.
Then circle the picture for each word I say.

Blending Onsets and Rimes

1.

2.

3.

4.

5.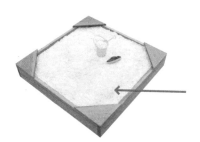

Say words in two parts to your child, for example, *c-ar.*
Have him or her blend the sounds to make a word.

28b Listen as I say some words in two parts.
Then circle the picture for each word I say.

Star Words: *at, and, like, go*

at   and   like   go

I __go__ to the playground.

I __like__ the playground.

Max __and__ Dan are __at__ the

playground.

29a | Trace the Star Words with your finger when you hear them. Draw a picture to go with the sentences.

Name _____

Reading Sentences with *at*, *and*, *like*, and *go*

⭐ **at** ⭐ **and** ⭐ **like** ⭐ **go**

1. The  is at the  .

2. The  is at the  .

3. The  go in the  .

4. The  and  like the  .

> 📖🏠 Ask your child to read the sentences to you, then describe the pictures.

29b | Read each sentence to a partner.

Firefly

The firefly
Goes flashing by,
A lemon-golden spark,
A dancing Rhinestone in the sky,
A jewel in the dark.

—Effie Lee Newsome

Ff

to

he

Ff Sf Ft Ff Ff Cf

30a Color the fish with partner letters *Ff*.
Then write the letters *Ff* on the lines.

Name _____

Initial Consonant /f/

Five funny friends feel fine.

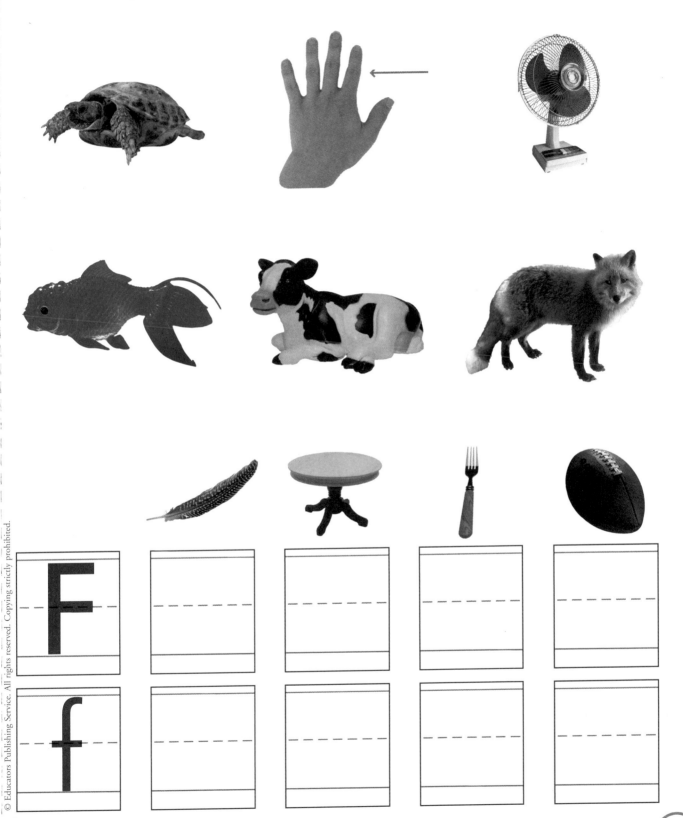

30b | (top) Cross out the pictures that do not begin with /f/. (bottom) If the picture's name begins with /f/, write the letters *Ff* on the line.

Baa, Baa, Black Sheep

Baa, baa, black sheep,
Have you any wool?
Yes, Sir, Yes, Sir, three bags full.

B b

you

 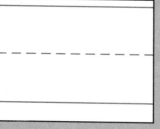 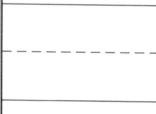

31a Color the boats with partner letters *Bb*.
Then write the letters *Bb* on the lines.

Initial Consonant /b/

Big boys burst balloons on beaches.

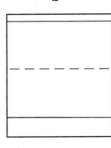  

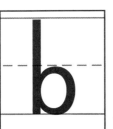  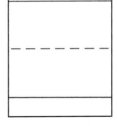 

B				
b				

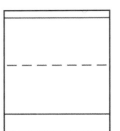 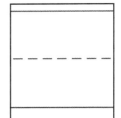 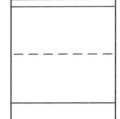

31b (top) Cross out the pictures whose names do not begin with /b/. (bottom) If the picture's name begins with /b/, write the letters *Bb* on the lines.

Mary Mary, Quite Contrary

Mary, Mary, quite contrary,
How does your garden grow?
With silver bells and cockle shells
And pretty maids all in a row.

in   and   a

32a   Color the moons that have the partner letters
Mm. Then write the letters *Mm* on the line.

Name _____

Initial Consonant /m/

Many monkeys make more money.

  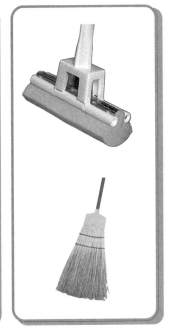 

M

m

| 32b | (top) Circle the picture on each card that begins with /m/. (bottom) If the picture's name begins with /m/, write the letters *Mm* on the lines. |

Daffodils

Daffy-down-dilly has come to town
In a yellow petticoat and a green gown.

Dd

is

and

a

33a Color the ducks with the partner letters *Dd*. Then write the letters *Dd* on the lines.

Name _____

Initial Consonant /d/
Donna's ducks dive deep down.

D

d

33b (top) Circle all the things in Donna's room that begin with /d/. (bottom) If the picture's name begins with /d/, write the letters Dd on the lines.

Rain, Rain, Go Away

Rain, rain, go away.
Come again another day.
Rob and Rachel want to play.

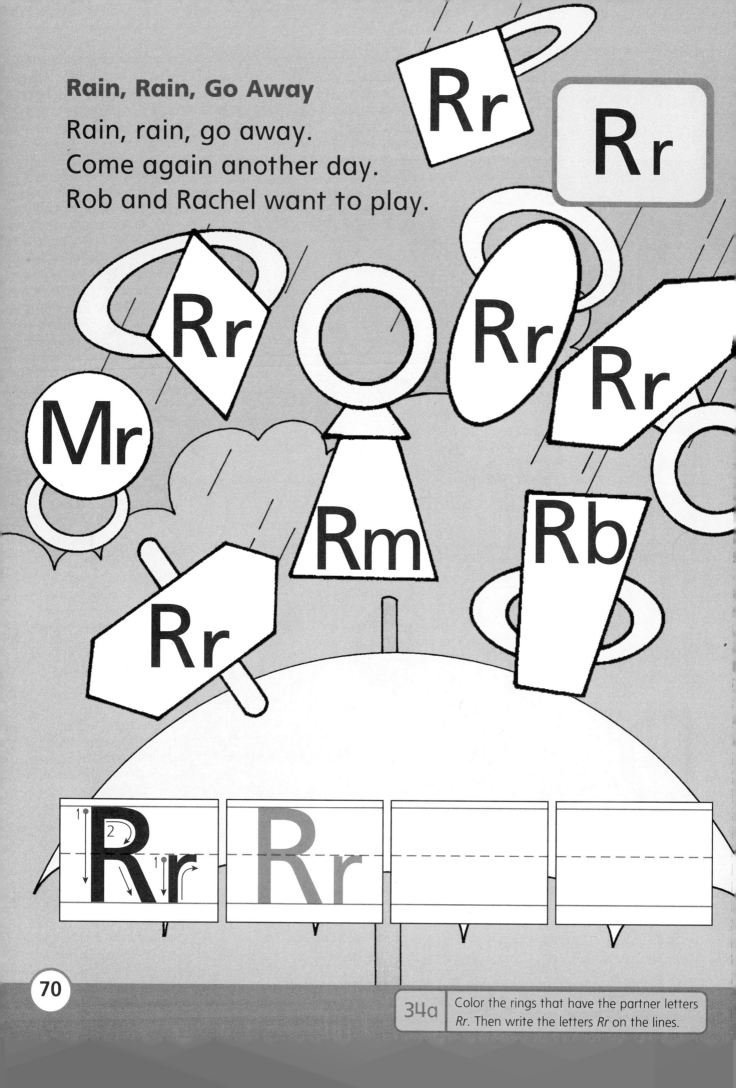

34a Color the rings that have the partner letters *Rr*. Then write the letters *Rr* on the lines.

Initial Consonant /r/
Real roosters rest on rooftops.

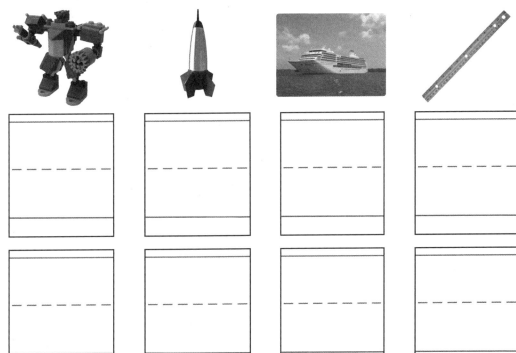

R

r

34b (top) Circle all the things that begin with /r/. (bottom) If the picture's name begins with /r/, write the letters Rr on the lines.

Review Initial Consonants /f/ and /b/

1.   f   b

2.   f   b

3.   f   b

4.   f   b

5.   f   b

6.   f   b

7.   f   b

8.   f   b

9.   f   b

10.   f   b

Make a list with two columns, one headed *F* and one *B*. Have your child look around the house and decide which column items should go in.

35a | Say each picture's name. Circle the *f* if it begins like *fish*. Circle the *b* if it begins like *boat*.

Name _____

Animal Friends

Help your child think of more animals, pets' names, etc., and group them by their beginning sounds.

35b Draw a line connecting the animals whose names begin with the same sound.

Review Initial Consonants /f/, /b/, /m/, /d/, and /r/

1.

2.

3.

4.

5.

 Have your child make up and tell you a story about one of the things pictured on this page.

36a Say the name of each picture in the first column. Circle the pictures in that row that begin with the same sound.

Name _____

Which One Doesn't Belong?

_____

- - - - - - - - - - - - -

_____

_____

- - - - - - - - - - - - -

_____

 Play "Which One Doesn't Belong?" with household items. Name
two or three that begin with the same sound and one that doesn't.

36b | In each group of pictures, cross out the one that does not begin with the same sound
as the other three. Then write the letter that begins the other three words on the line.

What Begins with A?

A is for *ant* who is busy and tiny
A is for *apple*, delicious and shiny
A is for *antelope*, who runs fast all day
Ant, apple, and antelope—
    each starts with A.

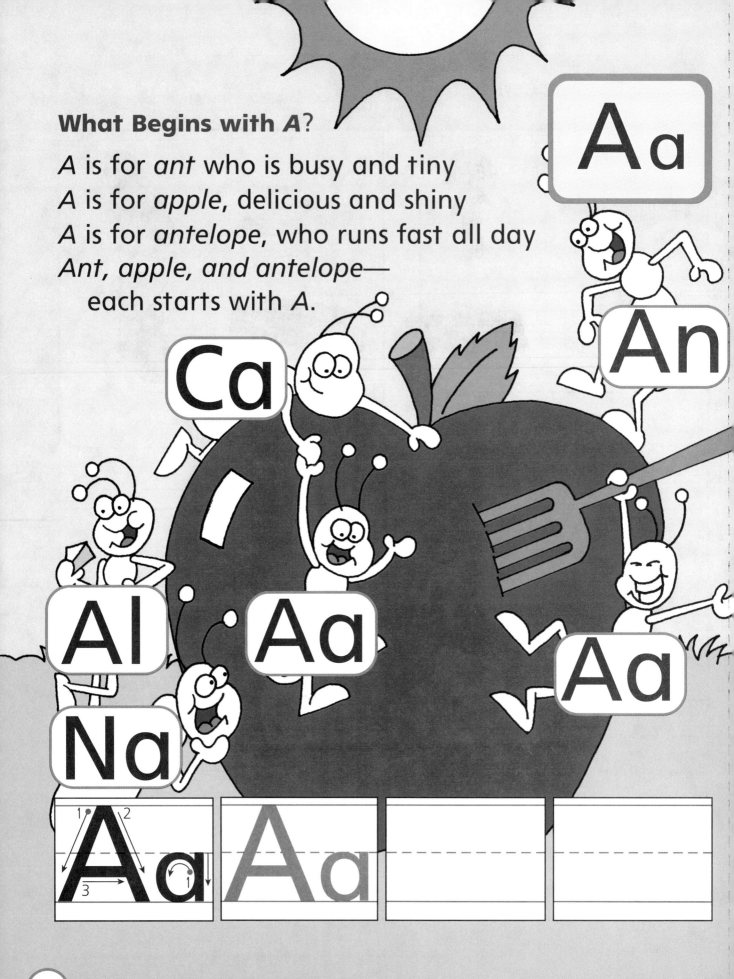

Color all the ants that have the partner letters *Aa* on them. Then write the letters *Aa* on the lines.

Initial Short *a*

Al the anteater ambled after ants.

  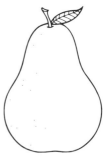

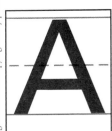  

A				
a				

37b (top) Color all the pictures whose names begin with short *a*. (bottom) If the picture's name begins with short *a*, write the letters *Aa* on the lines.

Blending Onsets and Rimes with Short *a*

1. b	➜	at		
2. c	➜	at		
3. r	➜	at		
4. s	➜	and	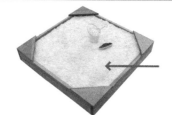	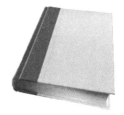
5. l	➜	and		
6. b	➜	and		

 Have your child show and tell you how to blend the letters to make the words on this page.

38a Say the name of the letter in the first column. Add *at* or *and* to make a word. Circle the picture for the word you make.

Name _____

Word Family -*at*

1. bat	 
2. mat	 
3. rat	 

C	S
_____ at	_____ at

38b | Circle the picture for each word. Then write the letters *f* and *s* to make two new words at the bottom of the page. Draw a picture for each new word.

Review Initial Short *a*

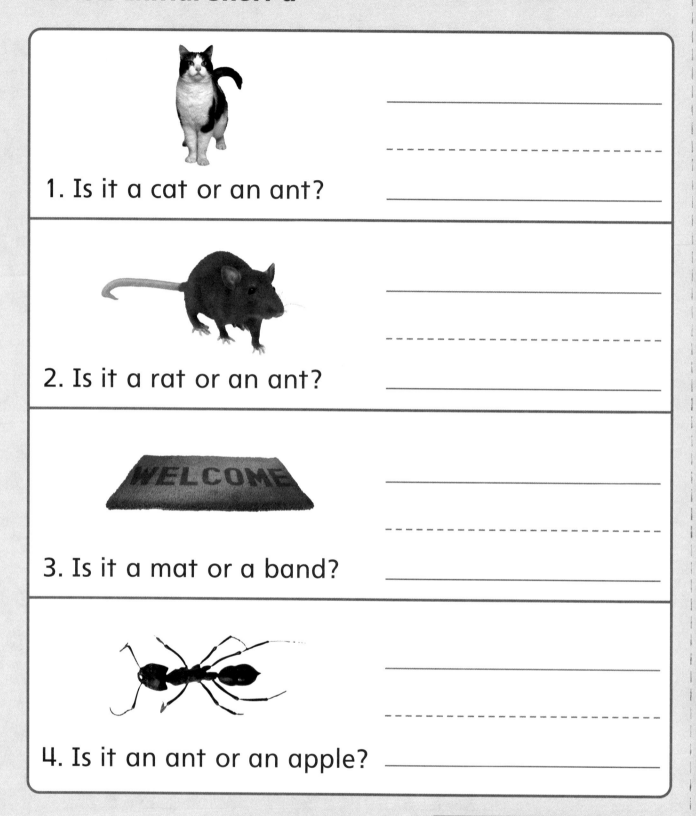

1. Is it a cat or an ant? _____

2. Is it a rat or an ant? _____

3. Is it a mat or a band? _____

4. Is it an ant or an apple? _____

Write the answer to the question on the line. Use the picture to help you.

Sam and the Cat

The cat ran.
Sam ran.
Sam and the cat ran.
Sam and the cat ran on the sand.
Sam and the cat ran fast.

39b Read the story "Sam and the Cat" with me.

Star Words: *it, to, he, you, she*

it   to   he   you   she

1.   to   you   to

2.   he   he   is

3.   she   it   it

4.   you   it   you

5.   he   she   she

1. You go to ⬛ on a 🚌 .

2. You go on it.

3. He is on the  .

4. She is on the  .

40a   (top) Circle the two words that are the same in each line. (bottom) Read the sentences.

Name _____

Reading *it, to, he, you, she*

it to he you she

1. You go to the  .

2. He is at the  .

3. She has a  .

4. It is .

Have your child practice reading these sentences to you.

40b Listen while I read the sentences. Trace the Star Words with your finger when you hear them.

Parent Letter

Dear Parents,

Your child's exciting reading journey continues. In school, your child is doing many things to get ready for first grade. At home, you can help your child down that important road.

During the next few weeks, your child will

- Learn more about the letters of the alphabet and the sounds of these letters in words

- Hear and enjoy stories and poems that the teacher will read

- Learn many new words and use these words when speaking to others

- Continue to learn more about our world with lessons in math, science, social studies, art, music, and other kindergarten subjects

You can help your child become a successful reader every step of the way. Keep doing the Phonics Plus exercises marked with this icon 📖, and you can continue to

- *Point out letters of the alphabet in your child's world.* Print is all around us. You can call attention to letters everywhere you go: on the street, at the mall, at the supermarket, in your own home.

- *Read to your child every day.* Share books that your child will enjoy. Let your child participate by pointing out words that he or she knows. Listen as your child shares a favorite book with you. Read alphabet books and find things that begin with each letter. Visit the library. Talk about the stories you read together.

- *Involve your child in tasks that include reading.* As you make out the grocery list, ask about the first letter (and sound) in the word *salt*. As you look up a telephone number, point out the letter that you need to find. As you read directions for cooking, let your child follow the print in the cookbook or on the back of the box as you read.

Finally, let your child see you reading. Children who see their parents reading learn to read more successfully themselves.

Before you know it, your child will be reading on his or her own!

Sincerely,

John F. Savage

Carta a los Padres

Queridos padres:

La emocionante aventura de su hijo/hija con la lectura continúa. En la escuela, está haciendo muchas cosas que le preparan para el primer grado. En casa, usted puede ayudarle a lograr ese importante objetivo.

Durante las siguientes semanas, su hijo/hija

- Profundizará en el aprendizaje de las letras del alfabeto y los sonidos de estas letras en palabras

- Escuchará y disfrutará con cuentos y poemas leídos por el maestro/la maestra

- Aprenderá muchas palabras nuevas y las utilizará al hablar con otras personas

- Seguirá aprendiendo acerca de nuestro entorno con clases de matemáticas, ciencias, estudios sociales, arte, música y otras materias del jardín de infancia

Puede ayudar a su hijo a desarrollar sus habilidades lectoras en cada paso del proceso. En casa, sigan realizando los ejercicios de Phonics Plus indicados con este símbolo 📖. Puede continuar :

- *Señalando las letras del alfabeto que aparecen en el entorno de su hijo/hija.* Hay letras impresas por todas partes. Puede llamar su atención hacia las letras allá donde vayan: en la calle, en el centro comercial, en el supermercado, en su propia casa.

- *Leyendo a su hijo/hija cada día.* Lean los libros que le gustarán. Anímele a participar señalando las palabras que ya conoce. Preste atención cuando su hijo/hija quiera leerle uno de sus libros favoritos. Lean libros sobre el alfabeto y busquen cosas que empiecen por cada letra. Vayan a la biblioteca. Hablen de los cuentos que lean juntos.

- *Involucrando a su hijo/hija en las tareas que requieran leer.* Cuando haga la lista de la compra, pregúntele la primera letra (y el sonido) de la palabra *sal*. Cuando consulte un número de teléfono, señale la letra que están buscando. Cuando lea instrucciones para cocinar, haga que él o ella siga el texto del libro de cocina o en la parte posterior del envase mientras usted lo lee.

Por último, haga que su hijo/hija le vea leer. Los niños que ven a sus padres leer se acaban convirtiendo en mejores lectores ellos mismos.

Antes de lo que se imagina, ¡su hijo/hija leerá por su cuenta!

Atentamente,

John F. Savage

Alphabet Rhymes

H h

H was once a little hen,
    Henny,
    Chenny,
    Tenny,
    Henny
Eggsy-any,
Little hen?

K k

K Was once a little kite,
    Kity,
    Whity,
    Flighty,
    Kity,
Out of sighty,
Little kite!

G g

G was once a little goose,
    Goosy,
    Moosy,
    Boosey,
    Goosey,
Waddly-woosy,
Little goose!

41b   Listen to these silly alphabet poems. Follow along with me.

This Little Piggy Went to Market

This little piggy went to market,
And this little piggy stayed home.
This little piggy had roast beef
And this little piggy had none.
And this little piggy went, "Whee, whee, whee!"
All the way home.

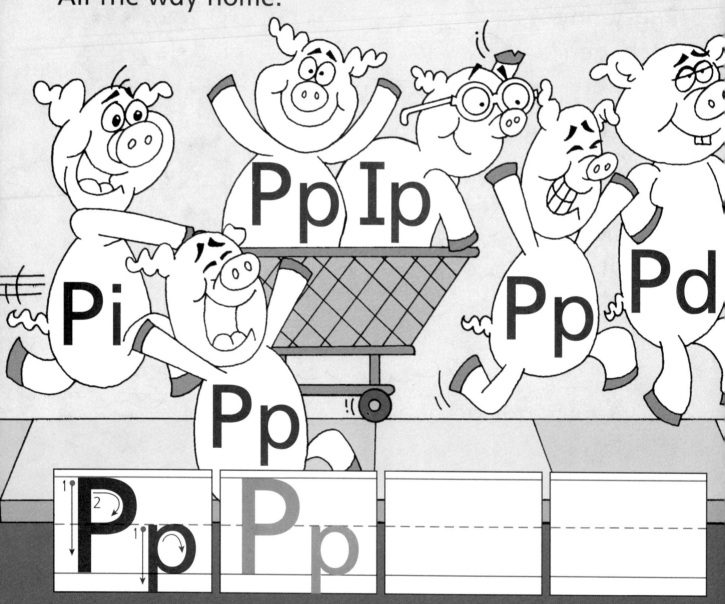

88

42a Color the pigs that have the partner letters *Pp*. Then write the letters *Pp* on the lines.

Name _____

Initial Consonant /p/

Peter Piper picked a
peck of pickled peppers.

P				
p				

42b (top) Circle the foods whose names begin with /p/. (bottom) If the
picture's name begins with /p/, write the letters *Pp* on the lines.

Hakeem

A happy young man named Hakeem
Went hiking and fell in a stream.
But his clothes were still dry
And he didn't know why.
Then he woke. He was having a dream!

43a | Color the hats with the partner letters *Hh*.
Then write the letters *Hh* on the lines.

Name _____

Initial Consonant /h/

Harry and Helen have a happy home high on a hill.

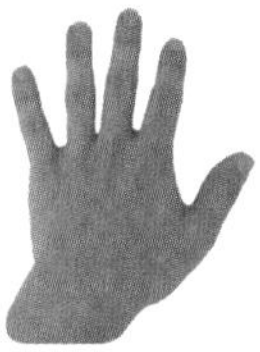

H

h

43b (top) Circle the pictures whose names begin with /h/. (bottom) If the picture's name begins with /h/, write the letters *Hh* on the lines.

King Boggen

King Boggen, he built a fine new hall,
Pastry and piecrust, that was the wall.
The windows were made of black
    pudding and white,
Roofed with pancakes, you never saw the like!

44a   Color the crowns that have the partner letters *Kk*. Then write the letters *Kk* on the lines.

Initial Consonant /k/

The king keeps keys in a kettle in the kitchen.

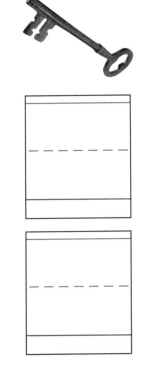

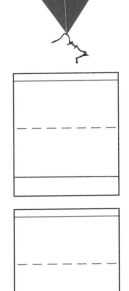

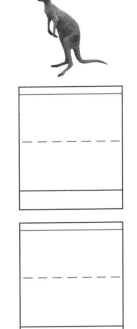

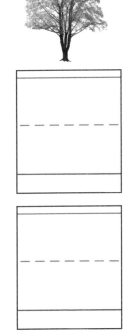

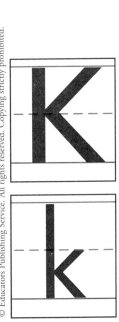

44b | (top) Circle the happy face if the two pictures both begin with /k/. Circle the sad face if they do not both begin with /k/. (bottom) If the picture begins with /k/, write the letters *Kk* on the lines.

Geese

I saw some geese go strutting by
With heads and necks held very high.
I saw six geese upon the lawn,
And each one had boots of orange on.

—Effie Lee Newsome

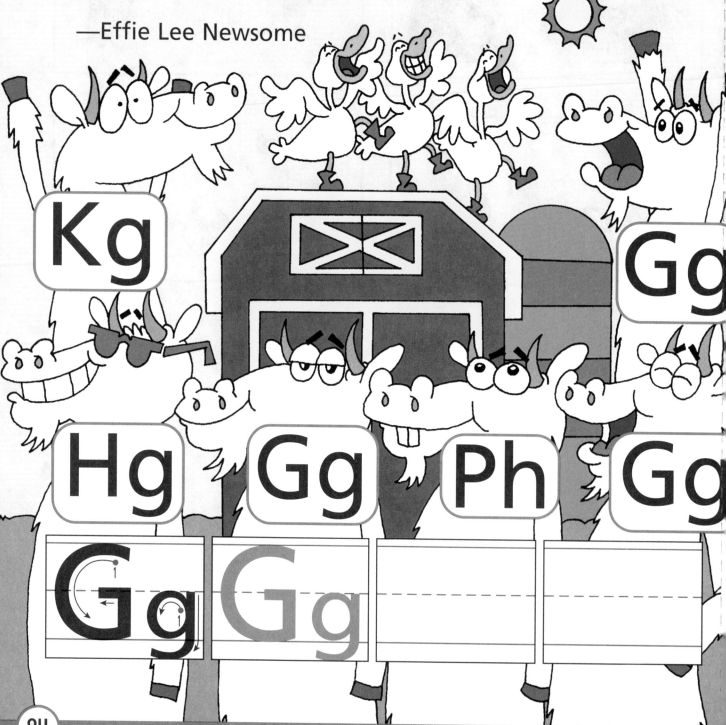

45a Color the goats that have the partner letters *Gg*. Then write the letters *Gg* on the lines.

Initial Consonant /g/

Good girls give grapes to goofy geese.

G
g

45b (top) Circle all the objects that begin with /g/ as in *goat*. (bottom) If the picture begins with /g/, write the letters *Gg* on the lines.

Vera

Vera, the bird in a vest,
Rested inside of her nest.
When the wind blew,
Away Vera flew,
'Til she came to a nice spot to rest.

46a Color the vans that have the partner letters *Vv*. Then write the letters *Vv* on the lines.

Initial Consonant /v/

Von's velvet vest is very vibrant.

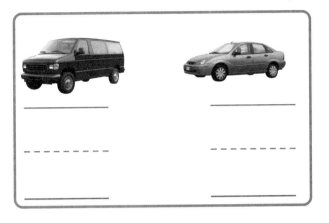

_____   _____

- - - - - -   - - - - - -

_____   _____

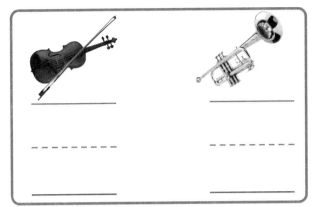

_____   _____

- - - - - -   - - - - - -

_____   _____

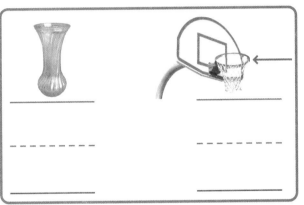

_____   _____

- - - - - -   - - - - - -

_____   _____

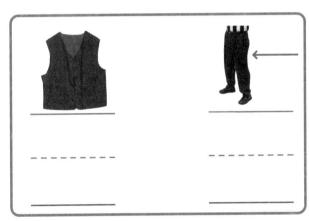

_____   _____

- - - - - -   - - - - - -

_____   _____

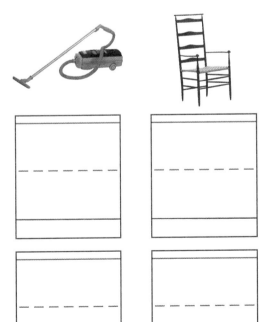

46b (top) Write the letter *v* under the picture in each pair that begin with /v/.
(bottom) If the picture begins with /v/, write the letters *Vv* on the lines.

Review Initial Consonants /p/ and /h/

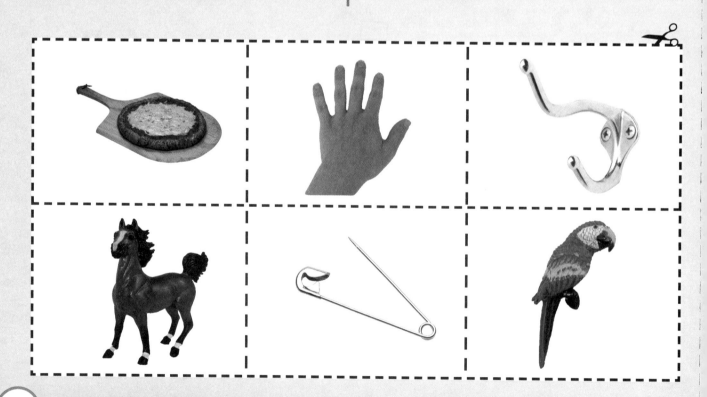

47a Cut out the pictures. If the picture's name starts with /p/, paste it under the pig. If it starts with /h/, paste it under the hat.

Name _____

Review Initial Consonants /k/, /g/, and /v/

47b | In each row, circle the two pictures that begin with the same sound. Then write the letter that represents that sound on the line.

Review Initial Consonants /p/, /h/, /k/, and /g/

P

H

K

G

48a Cut out the pictures. Paste the animals in the boxes according to the initial consonant sound in their names.

Name _____

Changing Letters, Changing Words

 p ➡ v

 c ➡ g

 k ➡ r

 k ➡ b

 m ➡ h

 Have your child talk through how he or she changed the words on this page by changing the beginning sound.

48b Say the name of the object in the first picture. Then change the first sound to make a new word. Circle the picture of the new word.

I Is for Igloo

I is for *igloo*, slippery and cold.
I is for *insect*, tiny but bold.
I is for *inside*, where I like to be.
Inside an igloo is where you'll find me.

I i

Ii

Li

Ia

Ii

Name _____

Initial Short *i*

Iggy inched his way into the igloo.

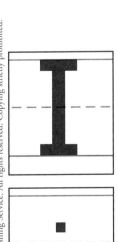   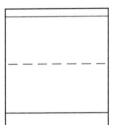

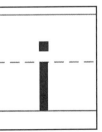  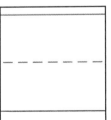

© Educators Publishing Service. All rights reserved. Copying strictly prohibited.

49b (top) Circle the pictures whose name begins with short *i*. (bottom) If the picture's name begins with short *i*, write the letters *Ii* on the lines.

103

Word Family -ip

s   l   r   t

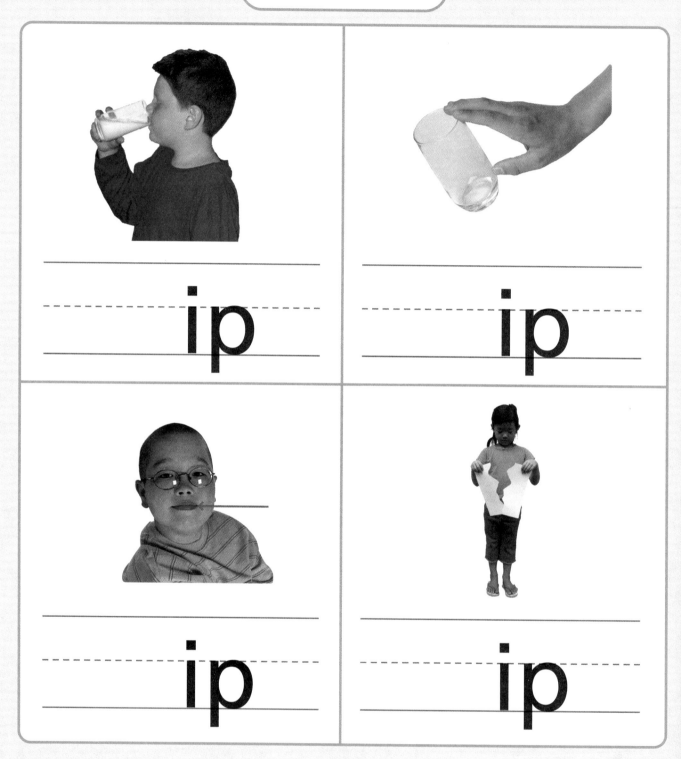

ip

ip

ip

ip

50a Say the names of the letters in the box with me. Use one of these letters to make a word for each picture.

Name _____

Blending Onsets and Rimes with Short *i*

1. s   →   it

2. h   →   it

3. f   →   in

4. p   →   in

 Have your child show you how she or he **blends the** words on this page.
Challenge your child to blend f/it, p/it and b/in, t/in and read the words to you.

50b | Say the sound of the letter in the first column. Add the word
family -*it* or -*in* to make a word. Circle the picture for the word.

Review Short *i*

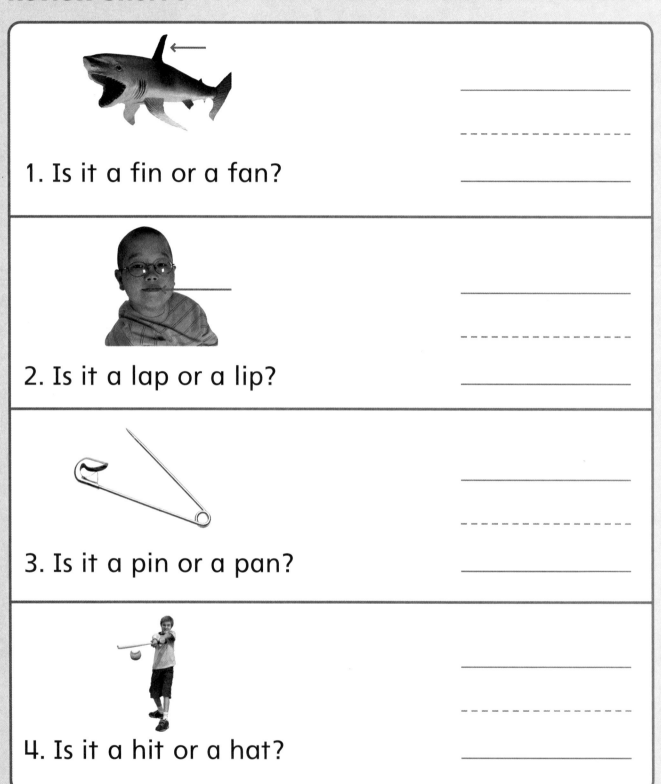

1. Is it a fin or a fan?

_____
- - - - - - - - - - - - - - -
_____

2. Is it a lap or a lip?

_____
- - - - - - - - - - - - - - -
_____

3. Is it a pin or a pan?

_____
- - - - - - - - - - - - - - -
_____

4. Is it a hit or a hat?

_____
- - - - - - - - - - - - - - -
_____

 Ask your child to read you the sentences on this page.
Then encourage him or her to practice writing the answers.

51a | Write the answer to each question on the line. Use the pictures to help you.

Sentences with Short *i*

A rip is in the cap. ● ●

I is for igloo. ● ●

The rat bit the tin. ● ●

A cat can sit. ● ●

 Ask your child to tell you a story based on one of the sentences on this page.

51b Draw a line from the picture to the sentence that tells about the picture.

Star Words: *with, are, of, I, make*

with   are   of   I   make

1.	make	make	are	_____
2.	of	with	of	_____
3.	make	I	I	_____
4.	of	with	with	_____
5.	are	I	are	_____

Circle the words that are the same in each row. Write that word on the line.

Reading Sentences with *with*, *are*, *of*, *I*, and *make*

1. The  is in the  .

2. The  is with a  .

3. She is  .

4. You and I run to the .

5. You and I make with the queen .

6. You and I are .

52b Read these sentences to a partner. Point to each word and picture as you read.

Uncle Ug

Uncle Ug is a funny guy,
Unbuttoned shirt and ugly tie.
His umbrella is upside down.
Children laugh as he walks through town.

53a Color the umbrellas with the partner letters *Uu*. Then write the letters *Uu* on the lines.

Initial Short *u*

Unhappy Uncle Ug is under an umbrella.

111

(top) Circle the happy face if the picture's name begins with short *u*. Circle the sad face if it does not. (bottom) If the picture's name begins with short *u*, write the letters *Uu* on the lines.

Word Family -ug

1. bug

2. mug

3. rug

4. hug

The bug has the rug. ●

Uncle Ug has a mug. ●

54a   1–4: Circle the picture for each word. (bottom) Read each sentence.
Draw a line from the sentence to the picture that it describes.

Name _____

Blending Onsets and Rimes with Short *u*

1. n　→　ut

2. b　→　ug

3. c　→　ut

4. m　→　ug

5. p　→　up

Listen to your child as she or he blends the words on this page. Challenge your child to blend b/ut, h/ut and d/ug, h/ug.

54b　Say the sound of the letter in the first column. Add the word family *-ut* or *-ug* in the second column to make a word. Circle the picture for the word you make.

Review Initial Short *u*

1. Is it a hut or a hat?

2. Is it a cut or a cup?

3. Is it a pup or a pin?

4. Is it a nut or a tub?

Ask your child to read you the sentences on this page.
Then encourage him or her to practice writing the answers.

55a Write the answer to the question on the line. Use the picture to help you.

Sentences with Short *u*

Uncle Ug has a cup.　●　　●

A nut is in the mug.　●　　●

The bug can tug a rug.　●　　●

The pup is in the hut.　●　　●

 Ask your child to tell you a story based on one of the sentences on this page.

55b | Draw a line from the picture to the sentence that tells about the picture.

Review Word Families *-at, -ip,* and *-ug*

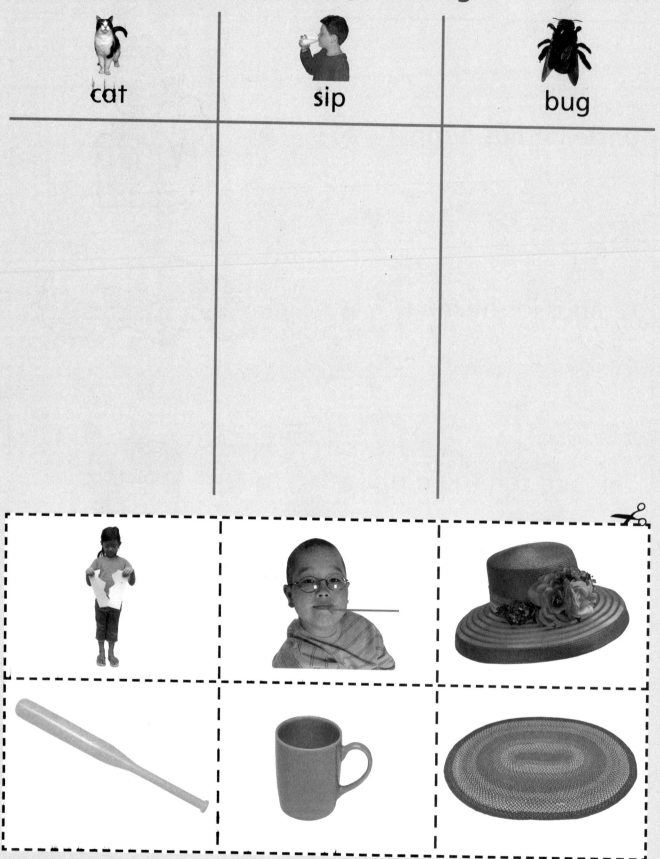

cat	sip	bug

56a Cut out the pictures. Paste them into the correct columns according to word families.

Name _____

Shoot the Ball

Aa

Ii

Uu

With your child, compile a list of words that begin with the sound of *a* as in apple, *i* as in inch, and *u* as in umbrella.

117

56b Draw a line from the picture to the correct basket.

Wicked, Wily Cat

Montague Michael
You're much too fat,
You wicked old, wily old,
Well-fed cat.

Wv

Ww

Ww   Ww   Mw

Wu   Ww

W₁w   Ww

Name _____

Initial Consonant /w/

Willy waited a week for a wet wave.

W

W

57b (top) Circle the five things in the shop that start with /w/. (bottom)
If the picture begins with /w/, write the letters *Ww* on the lines.

Jack Be Nimble

Jack be nimble, Jack be quick,
Jack jump over the candlestick.

Color the jars that have the partner letters *Jj*.
Then write the letters *Jj* on the lines.

Initial Consonant /j/

Jolly Jack jumps joyfully over jars of jelly.

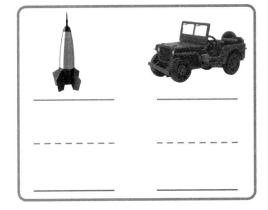

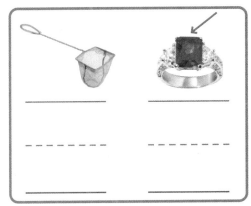

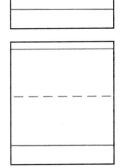

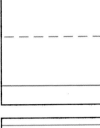
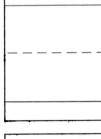

J				
j				

58b | (top) Write the letter *j* under the picture in each pair that starts with /j/.
(bottom) If the picture begins with /j/, write the letters *Jj* on the lines.

The Queen of Hearts

The Queen of Hearts,
She made some tarts,
All on a summer day.
The Knave of Hearts,
He stole the tarts,
And took them all away.

Qq

Qa

Qj

Qa

Ja

Qw

Qq

Qa

59a Color the queens that have the partner letters Qq. Then write the letters Qq on the lines.

Initial Consonants *qu* as /kw/

Quiet queens quickly make quilts.

59b (top) Circle the pictures whose names begin with /kw/. (bottom) If the picture's
name begins with /kw/ as in *queen*, write the letters *Qq* on the lines.

X and O

X and O, X and O,
I sign my notes like this.
O means that I send a hug
With X I send a kiss.

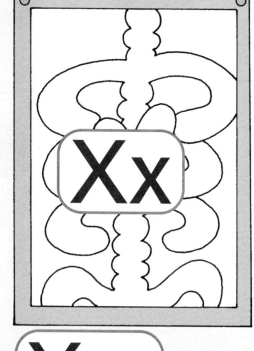

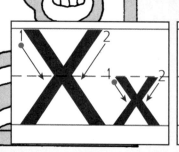

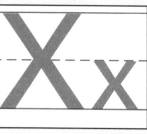

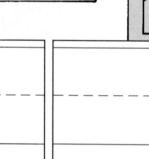

60a Color the x-rays that have the partner letters *Xx*. Then write the letters *Xx* on the lines.

Initial Consonant *x* as /eks/

X marks the spot of the extra x-ray.

60b Find and circle each letter *x* in this picture.

Yolanda Yak

Yolanda Yak, Yolanda Yak,
Has twenty yokes upon her back.
She walked to town.
Then turned around.
And she was tired when she got back.

Yq Xy Yy Yx Yy

61a   Color the yaks that have the partner letters *Yy*. Then write the letters *Yy* on the lines.

Name _____

Initial Consonant /y/

Young yellow yaks yell for a year.

127

61b (top) Draw a line from the pictures whose names begin with /y/ to the Y in the middle of the page. (bottom) If the picture's name begins with /y/, write the letters Yy on the lines.

Zippy Zebra

Here is Zippy Zebra,
He's standing in the zoo.
Every time you look at him,
He looks right back at you!

Zz

Zz

Qz

Yz

Zz

Zx

Zz

Zz

Zz

62a Color the zebras that have the partner letters Zz. Then write the letters Zz on the lines.

Name _____

Initial Consonant /z/

Zack the zebra zigzags through the zoo.

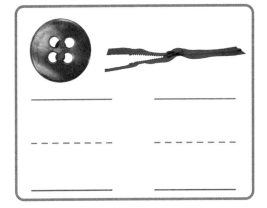

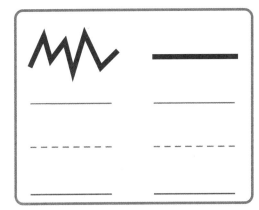

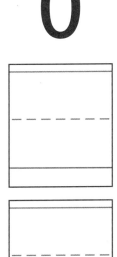

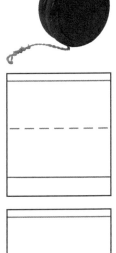

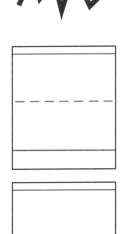

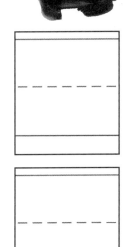

Z

z

62b (top) Write the letter z under the picture in each pair that starts with /z/. (bottom) If the picture begins with /z/ write Zz on the line.

Review Initial /w/ and /j/

63a If the picture's name begins with /w/, draw a circle around it.
If the picture's name begins with /j/, draw a square around it.

Name _____

Review Initial Consonants *qu* as /kw/,
Initial /y/ and /z/

Ask your child to use each of the following
words orally in a sentence: *queen, yo-yo, zebra.*

131

NOTES

Parent Letter

Dear Parents,

Your child is approaching the end of kindergarten. Soon your child will read on his or her own. What an exciting time!

As your child continues to make progress as a reader, your support at home remains important. There is much that you can do to help your child progress as a reader and writer. You should also help your child by working on the Phonics Plus exercises designed for you to do together at home. You can continue to:

- *Share books by reading aloud every chance you get.* Reading aloud remains one of the most important things that you can do to help your child learn to read. Select familiar books and let your child read parts of these books to you.

- *Play games involving the sounds in words.* Ask your child to think of words that rhyme with *coat* (*boat, note, goat, float,* and so on). Make up little rhymes, like *yummy, yummy in my tummy*. In sets of words like *cat, balloon,* and *cookie,* have your child guess which word doesn't belong with others based on the beginning sounds in the words. Have children clap to the rhythm or beat of language. These activities call attention to language sounds.

- *Focus on words* that begin with letter combinations like *sh* as in *sheep, ch* as in *chair, wh* as in *whale,* and *th* as in *thumb.* Ask your children to think of other words that begin with these sounds.

- *Review letters and sounds* that your child has learned. Remind him or her that *milk* starts with *m,* just like *mommy* and *Miguel.*

- *Help pick out words that your child can read.* Point out words that appear all around: in the kitchen, in the supermarket, in the neighborhood.

Finally, continue to talk about what your child is learning in school. Display the work that your child brings home and encourage his or her efforts.

Next year, in first grade, your child will continue the exciting journey into the world of reading and writing. Enjoy the journey together.

Sincerely,

John F. Savage

Carta a los Padres

Queridos padres:

El final del jardín de infancia se está acercando para su hijo/hija. Muy pronto leerá por su cuenta. ¡Qué época tan emocionante!

Mientras su hijo/hija sigue progresando en el desarrollo de sus habilidades lectoras, su apoyo de usted en casa sigue siendo importante. Usted puede hacer mucho para ayudarle a su hijo/hija a leer y escribir mejor. Debería ayudarle haciendo juntos los ejercicios de Phonics Plus diseñados para hacer en casa. Puede seguir :

- *Leyendo en voz alta libros siempre que tenga la ocasión.* Leer algo cada día en voz alta sigue siendo una de las actividades más importantes para ayudarle a su hijo/hija a aprender a leer. Seleccione libros conocidos y pídale que le lea partes de estos libros.

- *Jugando a juegos que conlleven los sonidos de las palabras.* Pídale a su hijo/hija que piense en palabras que riman con *camisa* (*risa, prisa, lisa, misa, etc.*). Inventen rimas, como *Sana sana, colita de rana; si no sanas hoy, sanarás mañana.* En series de palabras, como *gato, perro* y *gallina*, pídale que adivine la palabra que no pertenece al grupo en función del sonido inicial de las mismas. Haga que su hijo/hija aplauda/toque las palmas para marcar el ritmo del lenguaje. Estas actividades llaman su atención hacia los sonidos del lenguaje.

- *Concentrándose en las palabras* que empiezan por combinaciones de letras, como *cl* en *claro, cr* en *cream, br* en *Brasil* y *tr* en *tren.* Pida a su hijo/hija que piense en otras palabras que empiezan por estos sonidos.

- *Repasando las letras y los sonidos* que su hijo/hija ha aprendido. Recuérdele que *manzana* empieza por *m*, como *mamá* y *Miguel*.

- *Ayudándole a elegir palabras que él o ella pueda leer.* Señale las palabras que aparecen a su alrededor: en la cocina, en el supermercado, en el vecindario.

Por último, sigan hablando de lo que su hijo/hija está aprendiendo en la escuela. Exhiba los trabajos que traiga a casa y felicítele por su esfuerzo.

El año que viene, en el primer grado, su hijo/hija continuará el emocionante viaje que le llevará a descubrir el mundo de la lectura y la escritura. Disfruten del viaje juntos.

Atentamente,

John F. Savage

More Alphabet Rhymes

W w

W was once a whale,
    Whaly,
    Scaly,
    Shaly,
    Whaly,
Tumbly-taily,
Mighty whale!

Q q

Q was once a little quail,
    Quaily,
    Faily,
    Daily,
    Quaily,
Stumpy-taily,
Little quail.

J j

J was once a jar of jam,
    Jammy,
    Mammy,
    Clammy,
    Jammy,
Sweety, swammy,
Jar of jam!

64   Read these silly alphabet poems with me.

Ollie Ox and Octopus

Ollie Ox and Octopus,
    Climbed up a hill one day.
Ollie ate some olives,
    And Ostrich ran away.

136

Name _____

Initial Short o

An ox is observing an ostrich and an octopus

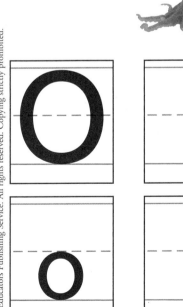

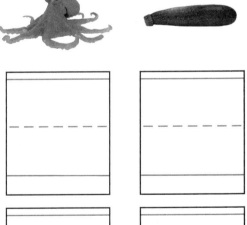

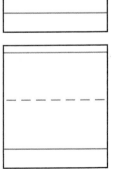

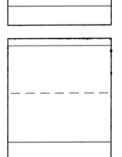

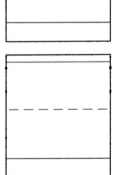

O

o

65b (top) Write the letter o under the picture in each pair that starts with short o.
(bottom) If the picture begins with short o write Oo on the line.

Word Family *-op*

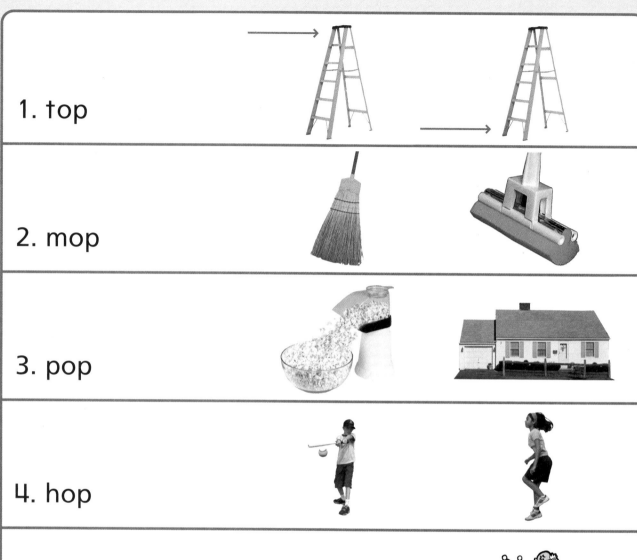

1. top

2. mop

3. pop

4. hop

5. The mug is on the top of the mop.

6. A bug can hop with pop.

66a | 1–4: Circle the picture for each word. 5–6: Read the sentences and draw a line from the sentence to the picture it describes.

Name _____

Blending Onsets and Rimes with Short o

1. b ➜ ox

2. d ➜ og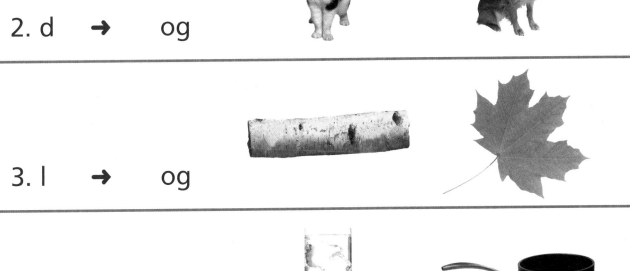

3. l ➜ og

4. p ➜ ot

5. f ➜ ox

 Have your child show you how she or he blends the words on this page. Challenge your child to blend p/ox, f/og and d/ot and read the words to you.

66b Say the sound of letters in the first column. Add the word family in the second column. Circle the picture of each new word you make.

Review Short o

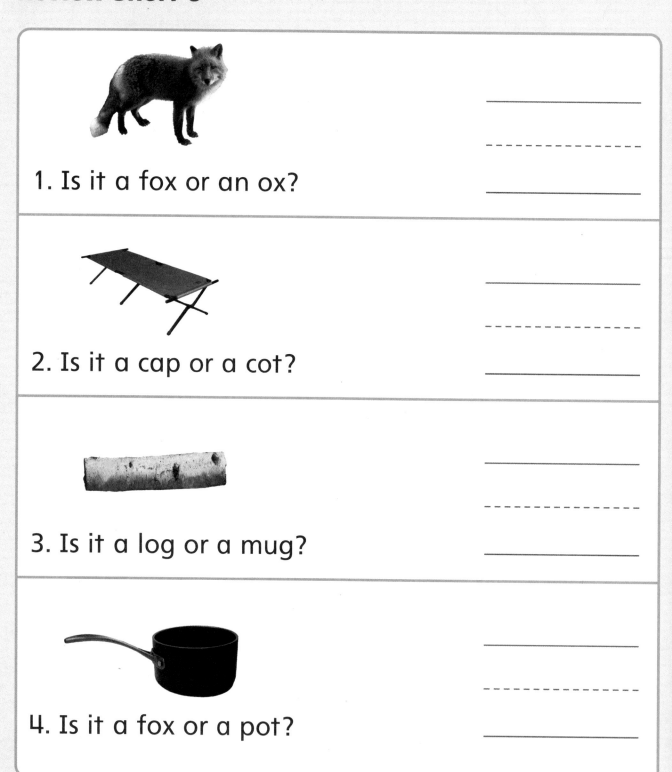

1. Is it a fox or an ox? _____

2. Is it a cap or a cot? _____

3. Is it a log or a mug? _____

4. Is it a fox or a pot? _____

 Ask your child to read you the sentences on this page. Then encourage him or her to practice writing the answers.

67a Write the answer to the question on the line. Use the picture to help you.

Sentences with Short o

The fox is with the dog. ●

The mop is in the box. ●

The pot is hot! ●

O is for ox. ●

 Listen as your child reads the sentences aloud to you. Discuss how the third sentence should be said with excitement, since it is followed by an !.

67b | Draw a line from the picture to the sentence that tells about the picture.

Review Star Words

with	are	of
are	with	of
are	of	with

_____

\- \- \- \- \- \- \- \- \- \- \- \- \-

_____

with	are	make
make	are	with
with	are	make

_____

\- \- \- \- \- \- \- \- \- \- \- \- \-

_____

I	with	I
with	I	with
of	of	of

_____

\- \- \- \- \- \- \- \- \- \- \- \- \-

_____

I	I	I
of	make	of
make	of	make

_____

\- \- \- \- \- \- \- \- \- \- \- \- \-

_____

with	are	make
are	with	make
with	are	make

_____

\- \- \- \- \- \- \- \- \- \- \- \- \-

_____

68a   Connect the three Star Words in a row in each game. Then write the "winning word" on the line under each game.

Review Star Words

it	to	he
to	it	he
to	he	it

_____

- - - - - - - - - - - - - -

_____

you	to	she
she	to	you
she	to	you

_____

- - - - - - - - - - - - - -

_____

it	she	it
she	it	she
he	he	he

_____

- - - - - - - - - - - - - -

_____

you	you	you
to	he	to
he	to	he

_____

- - - - - - - - - - - - - -

_____

you	it	she
you	it	she
it	you	she

_____

- - - - - - - - - - - - - -

_____

68b Connect the three Star Words in a row in each game.
Then write the "winning word" on the line under each game.

Eggs for Sale!

"Eggs for sale! Eggs for sale!"
     Yelled my little cousin.
"Eggs for sale! Eggs for sale!
     Fifty cents a dozen."

Ee

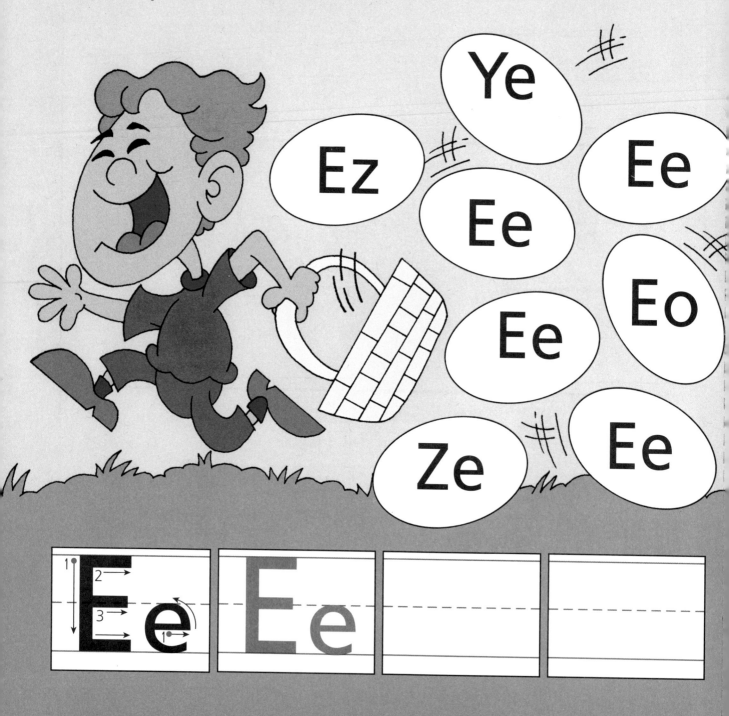

Color the eggs that have the partner letters *Ee*. Then write the letters *Ee* on the lines.

Name _____

Initial Short e

Edgar the elf dropped eggs off the elephant.

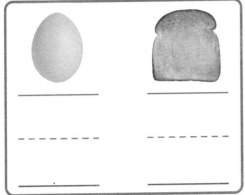

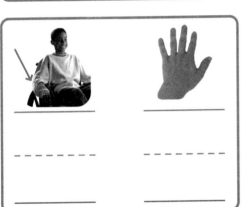

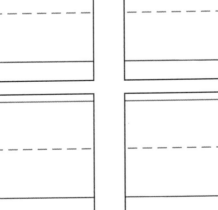

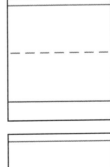
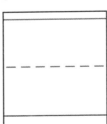

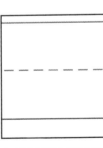

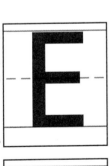

E

e

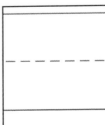

69b (top) Write the letter e under the picture in each pair whose name begins with short e. (bottom) If the picture's name begins with short /e/, write Ee on the line.

Word Family -en

1. hen

2. men

3. pen

4. Ben is with ten men. ●  ●

5. The hen has a pen. ●  ●

 Listen to your child practice reading sentences 4 and 5.

70a | 1–3: Circle the picture for each word. 4–5: Draw a line from each sentence to the picture it describes.

Blending Onsets and Rimes with Short *e*

1. b ➡ ed

2. j ➡ et

3. w ➡ et

4. r ➡ ed

5. n ➡ et

Listen to your child as she or he blends the words on this page. Challenge your child to blend f/ed, w/ed, m/et, and l/et.

70b Say the sound of each letter in the first column. Add the word family in the second column. Circle the picture of each new word you make.

Review Short e

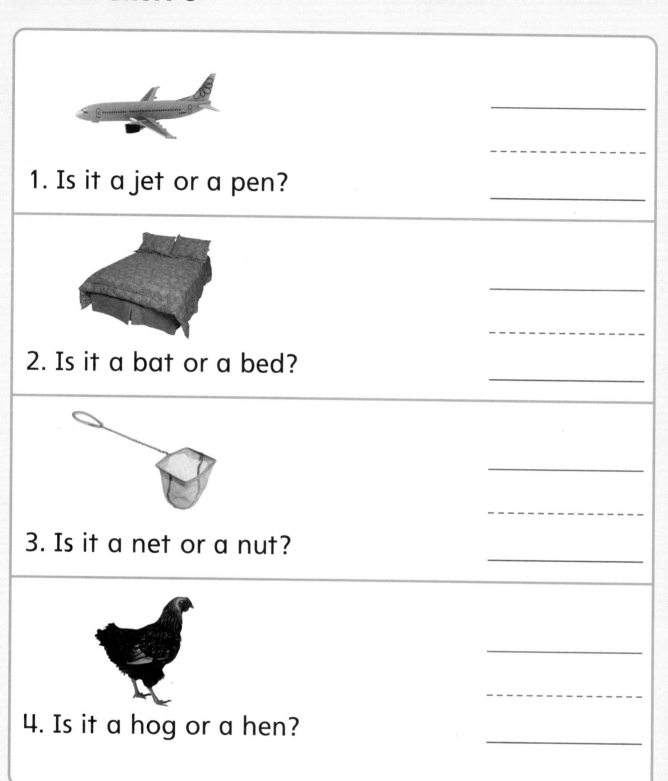

1. Is it a jet or a pen?

_____

- - - - - - - - - - - - -

_____

2. Is it a bat or a bed?

_____

- - - - - - - - - - - - -

_____

3. Is it a net or a nut?

_____

- - - - - - - - - - - - -

_____

4. Is it a hog or a hen?

_____

- - - - - - - - - - - - -

_____

 Ask your child to read you the sentences on this page.
Then encourage him or her to practice writing the answers.

71a | Write the answer to the question on the line. Use the picture to help you.

Sentences with Short e

E is for egg. ● ●

Ben met Ned at
the box of sand. ● ●

The fox is in the den. ● ●

Ken can get a net. ● ●

71b | Draw a line from the picture to the sentence that tells about the picture.

The Rabbit and the Turtle

"I am the fastest animal around," said the rabbit. "Who would like to race me?"

"I will," answered the turtle. The rabbit laughed. "OK," the rabbit said. "Let's go." The two animals went to the starting line.

"On your mark, get set, GO!"

The rabbit sped away. The turtle plodded along.

Soon, the rabbit was far ahead of the turtle. "I think I'll take a rest," the rabbit thought. And he lay down by the side of the road and fell asleep. The rabbit slept for a long, long time.

In a while, the turtle crawled by, past the rabbit as he slept. She looked at the rabbit and kept moving slowly along.

After a while, the rabbit woke up. "Oh, dear," he said. "I must finish the race!"

He started running again. But when he got near the finish line, what do you think he saw? The turtle was already crossing the line.

The turtle had won the race!

Name _____

The Rabbit and the Turtle: Sequencing

_____

- - - - - - - - - - - - -

_____

_____

- - - - - - - - - - - - -

_____

_____

- - - - - - - - - - - - -

_____

_____

- - - - - - - - - - - - -

_____

 Talk about your day with your child. Discuss what happened first, next, and so on.

151

72b Write the number 1 under the first thing that happened. Write 2 under the second thing. Write 3 under the next thing. Write 4 under the last thing.

Walk in the Country

a b c d e f

73a In each circle, write the first letter of that picture's name.

Walk in the Country

g h i j k l

153

73b | In each circle, write the first letter of that picture's name.

m n o p q r s

74a | In each circle, write the first letter of that picture's name.

Walk in the City

t u v w x y z

ABE'S MOVING COMPANY

155

74b In each circle, write the first letter of that picture's name.

Initial Consonant Digraph /sh/

1.

2.

3.

4.

5.

Help your child "collect" words beginning with the *sh* sound and list them. Help your child practice reading them accurately.

75a Circle the picture in each row that begins with /sh/ as in *sheep*.

Name _____

Initial Consonant Digraph /ch/

1.

2.

3.

4.

5.

 With your child, discuss other *ch* and *sh* things that Charlie might chew or find around the house, for example, *cheese, chili, shampoo, shutters*.

157

Initial Consonant Digraph /th/

1. 3   4

2.

3.

4.

5.

76a   Circle the picture in each pair that begins with /th/ as in *thumb*.

Initial Consonant Digraph /wh/

1.

2.

3.

4.

5.

 Play "Who am I thinking of?" with your child. Have the child ask questions about the mystery person by asking "wh" questions: *where*, *when*, and *what*.

76b Circle the picture in each row that begins with /wh/.

Review Initial Consonant Digraphs /sh/ and /ch/

77a | Some of these words begin with /sh/ as in *sheep*. Some begin with /ch/ as in *chair*. Cut out the pictures and paste them in the correct column.

Name _____

Review Initial Consonant Digraphs /th/ and /wh/

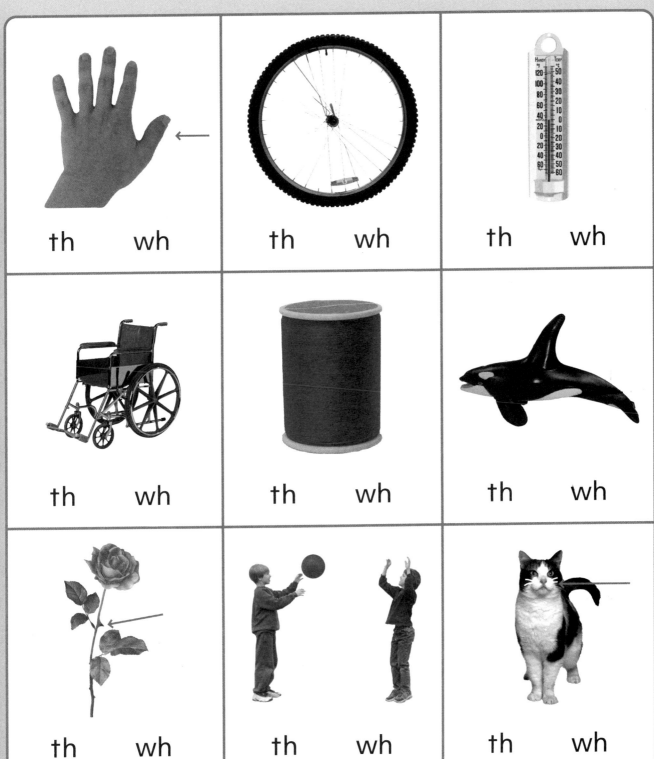

th wh	th wh	th wh
th wh	th wh	th wh
th wh	th wh	th wh

 Find several words that begin with *th* or *wh* sounds in **print material**, cut them out, and have your child sort them by beginning sound.

77b Look at these pictures. Circle the letters *th* if the first sound of the word is the same as *thumb*. Circle the letters *wh* if the first sound is the same as *whale*.

Review Initial Consonant Digraphs
/sh/, /ch, /th/, and /wh/

sh   ch   th   wh

sh   ch   th   wh

sh   ch   th   wh

78a   Write the letter combination under each word that begins with that sound.

Name _____

Blending Onsets and Rimes with Digraphs

ch ➜ in

sh ➜ in

th ➜ in

ch ➜ at

 Have your child show you how she or he blends the words on this page. Challenge your child to blend ch/at, sh/ip, th/at, and wh/en and read the words to you.

78b | Say the sound of the letters in the first column. Add the word family *-in* or *-at* in the second column to make a word. Circle the picture for the word you make.

Star Words Dominoes

the	and	for	on	you
have	it	a	in	he

in	is	of	at	with
at	for	like	and	of

to	he	are	I	is
I	with	go	have	has

the	you	a	are	on
like	she	has	make	go

79a Read the Star Words on the dominoes. Cut them out and match them to make a long line of words.

Name _____

Reading Sentences with Star Words

A  is in the  .

A  is on the  .

A  is on the .

79b Read these sentences. Then draw a picture about the ladybug.

Rhyming Words

1.

2.

3.

4. **3**

5.

6.

 Ask your child to find the pictures on this page that rhyme with *nail, two, bear, knee, sleep,* and *mop.*

80a | Listen while I read the questions to you. Then circle the correct picture.

Initial Consonant Digraph Substitution

sh ➜ ch

ip

 ch ➜ sh

op

 sh ➜ ch

in

80b Say the name of the object in the first picture. Then change the first sound of the word. Write the new word on the line.

Review Consonant Digraphs

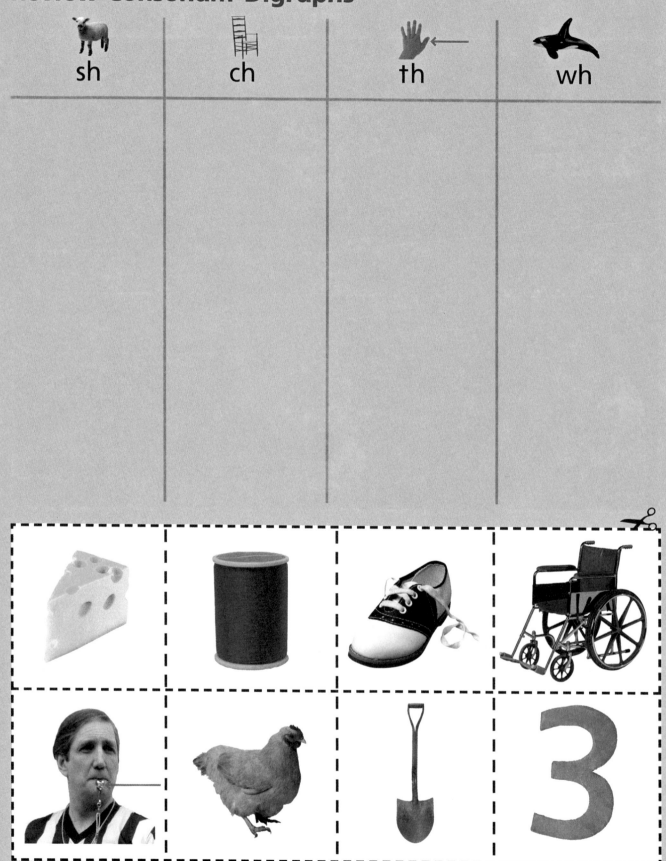sh	ch	th	wh

81a Cut out the pictures. Paste each picture under the picture with the same initial digraph.

Review Syllables

Chocolate
One, two, three, cho-
One, two, three, -co-
One, two, three, -la-
One, two, three, -te.
Stir, stir the chocolate.

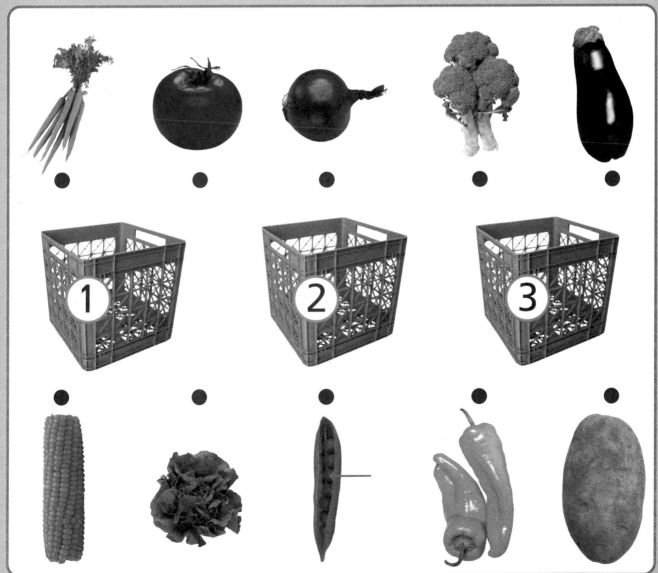

81b | Listen as I read this poem. Then draw a line from each vegetable to the correct vegetable bin according to the number of syllables.

Review Word Families

hen	mop	bug

82a Cut out the pictures. Paste each picture under the correct word family.

Review Initial Short Vowels

Ask your child to write the vowel that begins these words: *uncle*, *ink*, *elm*, *on*, and *add*.

82b Write the letter each picture begins with underneath it.

How To Make a Pizza

First, roll the dough into a circle.
Then, pour on tomato sauce.
Next, sprinkle cheese on top.
Then, add toppings,
Finally, put the pizza in the oven.
When it's ready, eat it.
Pizza is yummy!

Circle the things that are used to make pizza.

What do you do to pizza when it is finished?

Name _____

How to Make a Pizza: Sequencing

‾ ‾ ‾ ‾ ‾ ‾ ‾ ‾

‾ ‾ ‾ ‾ ‾ ‾ ‾ ‾

‾ ‾ ‾ ‾ ‾ ‾ ‾ ‾

‾ ‾ ‾ ‾ ‾ ‾ ‾ ‾

 Have your child tell you what he or she did today, putting the events in the order they happened.

173

83b Write the number 1 next to the first thing you do to make a pizza. Write 2 for the second thing. Write 3 for the next thing. Write 4 for the last thing.

84a | Color this picture.

Star Word Wall

the	is	he
you	have	

84b Add as many Star Words as you can to the Word Wall.

HOORAY

A a
B b
C c
D d
E e
F f
G g
H h
I i
J j
K k
L l
M m
N n
O o

X-RAY

Name _____

177

| 85 | With a partner, find a picture that begins with each letter. |

Celebrate Rhyme

Tree Bear
Listen to the tree bear
Crying in the night
Crying for his mommy
In the pale moonlight.

Jack and Jill
Jack and Jill went up the hill
To fetch a pail of water
Jack fell down
And broke his crown
And Jill came tumbling after.

Skyscraper
Skyscraper, skyscraper,
Scrape me some sky:
Tickle the sun
While the stars go by.

Celebrate Rhyme

Hickory Dickory Dock

Hickory dickory dock,
The mouse ran up the clock,
The clock struck one
The mouse ran down.
Hickory dickory dock.

Two Little Eyes

Two little eyes to look around,
Two little ears to hear each sound:
One little nose to smell what's sweet,
One little mouth that likes to eat.

86 Listen while I read these poems.

NOTES

NOTES

NOTES

NOTES